COMBATING DEPRESSION

Managing Your Depression Through Self-Care

Tiffany Walton

Tiffany Walton

Contents

Tiffany Walton

Introduction

I thought I was going to die. This was my initial feeling to the words "your COVID-19 test results came back positive." I became dizzy and almost passed out. Did I hear what she said correctly? Was this a mistake? Maybe my results were someone else's, or my test was contaminated. What about the people I had been around? Is my family going to get it? After going through so many traumatizing things this year, I had to have the worst luck in the world.

I could barely catch my breath. All I could do was panic and worry. I was already falling into depression as I continued to mourn the loss of my grandmother, who died just two weeks before. Crying myself to sleep almost every night, this diagnosis and all the hurt I was experiencing were not a good combination, but I recognized this pain, and I knew how to handle it.

Have you ever been in a hole lost, alone, worried, isolated, and depressed? It is a pretty dark place, and we do not know how we are going to pull ourselves out of it. We often recognize that we are suffering from depression, but we do not understand how we are going to cope.

The author has spoken with several people who do not have access to mental health care due to its affordability. Other individuals told her that they had terrible experiences speaking to mental health care workers, who lacked social and ethical diversity as health care providers. Many times, people wanted to talk to providers who looked like them or experienced similar issues.

Actively serving in the military, Tiffany views negative opposition to living a healthy life as "combat." She wrote this book because she had enough of seeing her brothers and sisters in arms, and a nation of people struggle with depression with no resources for help. She has witnessed warriors and friends succumb to depression and battled with it for almost twenty years.

This book will explain ten of the simplest steps that Tiffany created to help you manage your problems with depression. She coined the steps as the Combating Depression process and used them herself, before including them in this book. Some steps have exercises at the end of each chapter that you will find beneficial.

You will learn natural alternatives to medication to combat depression. The author experienced and prevailed over many issues that you, as a reader, have or might face in the future, and she wants to use her experiences to help all that she can.

The author is no stranger to depression, attempting to manage it for almost two decades. She reached the pinnacle of her depression after a recent diagnosis with COVID-19 and understood that she was not going to recover without putting up the most challenging fight of her life. Realizing that she had followed concrete steps to manage and prevent depression and that she had offered those steps to others in managing their depression, she had to finish this book to help others who struggle to do the same.

This book dives into natural techniques you can use to manage depression. However, they should not be used to diagnose, cure, or in opposition to a doctor's recommendation. No matter who you are, and whether you have access to mental health care, the Combating Depression process ensures that you have effective tools to prevent or manage your depression.

Let us begin our journey!

Chapter 1

The Day Our World Changed Forever

On March 14, 2020, my husband, son, and I boarded Southwest Airlines flight WN465 from Honolulu to Big Island Hawaii for a five-day mini vacation. Scheduled more than a year before and rescheduled several times due to the volcano eruptions and less than favorable climate conditions on the Big Island, we were excited to fly the friendly skies to our destination finally.

I do not watch the news much; however, a week or so before our trip, I started to hear about a deadly virus that broke out in China. Global speculation claimed that the virus came from a bat delicacy. Many described the virus as being similar to the flu, but deadly. I began to hear of deaths from the virus spreading in places like China, South Korea, and Italy. The coronavirus also began spreading throughout the United States.

As we boarded our flight, I received a text message from one of my coworkers stating that the military had placed service members on restricted travel due to the coronavirus. My heart sank, and I started panicking as I gazed wide-eyed at my husband. I did not know what to do, and I did not want to get in trouble for leaving the island of Oahu, Hawaii, but we had already boarded the plane.

Upon landing in Big Island, Hawaii, I received another text message stating that inter-island travel would still be permitted, which was great news for us. The coronavirus was spreading like wildfire across the world, and social media was there to keep us up to date with new details surrounding the deadly disease.

I could hardly enjoy my spring break and had a panic attack in my room one of the nights before bed. I could not seem to catch my breath. My throat felt swollen, and I experienced labored breathing. I was scared and did not understand why I was having trouble breathing. I began to catastrophize, speculating that I might have the deadly coronavirus. I would lay in bed, terrified until I somehow (with the comfort of my husband) fell asleep.

I was getting all the play-by-play updates on the coronavirus from social media, family, and friends. Articles and streams appeared on social media with notifications that celebrities had contracted the virus, which now had the medical name COVID-19. Conspiracies began to emerge that the government was behind the virus, China purposely leaked the virus, and the New World order was here. Martial law had arrived. 5G radiation would kill us all. Jesus was on the way back. The world would end. Whatever conspiracy theory, one could dream of was spreading around the world, causing mass hysteria and panic.

I vividly recall the fear that made itself a home in my mind on the day we returned to the island of Oahu, Hawaii. I instantly became afraid of and offended by anyone who coughed. The nerve of anyone who coughed near me! I did not want this deadly disease, and I certainly did not want my children to get it. I was frightened to board the plane with re-circulating air.

Upon my return home, I was informed by my employer that the local Hawaiian government made it mandatory for anyone who traveled off the island to quarantine for fourteen days. We could only leave our home for essentials, which I abided by. After a few days in our quarantine, the city shut down completely. I watched the island of Oahu, Hawaii, and the rest of the United States roll out a stay-at-home order.

COMBATING DEPRESSION

I had not felt this helpless since September 11, 2001. My youngest son was on spring break from high school when the pandemic initially began to spread. He did not return to school, and we witnessed education systems across the country shut down. I watched businesses close their doors, sending millions into unemployment.

The initial period of quarantine was difficult for me, and I can imagine it was the same for you and other families across the world. Together we experienced the panic-buying of toilet paper, while our children could no longer partake in the social environment of schools with friends and teachers. Some of you are or were in abusive relationships that increased in violence due to the shelter-in-place orders. With school closures, thousands of children (already in unsafe environments) started to experience an increase in mental, physical, sexual abuse, and neglect.

There are now families who are unable to pay their bills, buy food, or maintain the lifestyles they had just months ago. I heard an appalling statistic that 30 million people are now unemployed across the United States. By the time I publish the book you are reading, I imagine that number will increase significantly, with more than half of the United States struggling to find employment.

As you can imagine, the sudden abrupt change in life affected me in the same way that it has affected millions. Initially, the pandemic sent me into a state of depression, which unfortunately is familiar territory for me. Not only was I feeling depressed due to the pandemic, but I also began to reflect on the rock bottoms in my life. The places in my life that were so low that at times I did not want to live.

I knew that I never wanted to return to those lows, and I reflected on the idea that I had pulled myself out of that hole, and there was no reason to fall back in. I also thought about the millions of you who are now suffering from depression, and I attempted to figure

3

out what I could do to assist and help as many people as I could. The results of my thoughts on how I could help individuals suffering from depression helped create this book, and I genuinely hope that it will provide you with assistance in controlling any depression you may be experiencing. Know that even with the murky state of affairs the entire world is now undergoing, I am here with you. I send you light, even when it appears that our days are dark.

Chapter 3

Rock Bottom

I do not want to make this book about me, but I do want to make sure that you understand that I am speaking to you from experience. I also support the idea that my experiences qualify me to help you. Many will disagree, but I tend to seek advice from those who have experienced and beat the same challenges I may experience in life because I believe they are best suited to help me with my personal issues and even goals. Why not use someone else's triumphant experiences with depression to learn how to manage your own depression?

I will not degrade the education or health care systems; both are necessary and respected institutions in our society. I have sought mental health treatment for the past eleven years and feel that it was beneficial; however, I ask all the providers I see the same question. "Have you experienced the issue I am going through?" I ask this question because it is my opinion that I cannot thoroughly assist anyone with anything I have not experienced. I take the providers who admit that they have experienced depression more seriously than the ones who have not. I think of it as college versus on-the-job training. Nothing can replace the experience itself.

I want to be transparent with you and describe hitting my "rock bottom" while depressed. Earlier, I mentioned that the current pandemic caused me to revisit the "familiar territory" of depression. Still, I want you to understand that depression is something I have battled with my entire life. I am a problem-solver and will make myself vulnerable to help you or anyone else that I can. I am managing my depression with ease by sticking to the Combating Depression process I will explain in the upcoming chapters, and I believe I am qualified "through experience" to help you.

I cannot recall life ever being easy for me, and I started my journey at a deficit with an abundance of pitfalls. Born in 1980, I grew up in a town the world still refers to as the murder capital. I was raised in a single-parent home. My parents divorced when I was two years old, and I spent a lot of time at my grandmother's home. My granny is "The Strongest Woman, I Know." As a young girl, I watched her work and care for her two aging parents, my two grandfathers (her husband and ex-husband) who were both alcoholics, a mentally disabled great uncle, three uncles who struggled with alcohol and drug addiction, and my mother who was ill and suffered from epilepsy.

I grew up in a very toxic environment. Outside the home, I was exposed to sex at an early age, drugs, and violence. Most of my childhood friends had sexual encounters by age ten. Many of those encounters were older men within and outside their families. Most of the friends I went to elementary school with are now deceased. As a child, I was raised around relatives who were pedophiles. In my childhood household setting, toxicity was the norm.

As an adolescent with a lot of unsupervised time, I became a teen mother. I entered into toxic relationships, one after the other, and abuse came with the territory of those relationships. I am certain that I may have suffered from anxiety and depression as a child, teenager, and adult. I grew up feeling alone and insecure and never felt protected. My childhood trauma bled over into my teenage years as well as my adult life.

reiterate that I have sought medical assistance and found it beneficial. Please do not use this book as a substitution for professional mental health diagnosis and treatment.

In recent months, COVID-19 has wreaked havoc across the world. Our lives will never be the same. We are experiencing life; unlike anything we have ever seen before. As I previously mentioned, many of us went into a state of depression, and thousands, if not millions, of us, have not recovered.

At the beginning of the global pandemic, depression attempted to pay me another visit. I recall feelings of panic, fear, and sadness. For a couple of days after returning from my Big Island vacation, I would lie in bed continuously feeling helpless, trapped, afraid, and even claustrophobic. I began to rehearse all the negativity in my life and my past, and then something significant happened. I began self-talk and meditation on the good things in my life.

I got out of my bed, got dressed, and went outside. I started to walk, focusing on the sun, trees, and grass. Living in Hawaii, I found myself standing at the ocean, reflecting on how I had pulled myself out of one of the lowest seasons of depression that I had ever experienced.

Not only had I pulled myself out of a deep state of depression in the past, I also documented the specific steps I used to combat my depression, and I was now unconsciously utilizing that process. I quietly rejoiced while I marveled at the scene of the ocean and realized I had used my documented steps for over two years. I also began writing this book almost two years ago, and then life happened.

Most of us would agree that 2020 has been the worst year we have experienced—that is certainly how I feel. We do not know what to expect next, and right now, it seems like it could not get any worse than it already is. It is August, and, personally, I am over 2020.

Let me briefly tell you all about my year so far. The first few months I was fighting as the plaintiff in a legal proceeding. I was ill with the flu in February. I learned that my grandmother's (whom I often viewed as my second mom) breast cancer returned. Her cancer also spread into her chest cavity. In March, I was introduced to COVID-19 with the rest of the world. During April, I was confined to my home—what we now refer to as quarantine— and while being groomed, my dog's foot was broken.

In addition, in the same month, my oldest son was severely ill and bedridden for a month. In May, a law firm attacked the legitimacy of my business. In June, my grandmother's health turned for the worst, and she was hospitalized. July was the worst month of my life. I paid the IRS $7,000.00, had a birthday trip planned to Mexico, but instead headed to Gary, Indiana, where my grandmother succumbed to her illness on the 4th of July.

After returning to my home in Hawaii, I spent my birthday sicker than I have even been in my entire life. I was diagnosed with COVID-19, and I am still recovering. Not to mention my grandmother's estate is not settled, and that has become an ongoing family battle.

You may ask, "So what is your point?" My point is that so far, I have been through what I would refer to as "hell and back," but I held true to my stance that I would never let depression control me. In navigating 2020 up to this point, I have used everything that previously helped me combat my depression, and I have been able to stay afloat naturally. I am finding a way to smile and push on by using the process that I established and very much so believe in. I am still standing and intend to keep it that way.

Most importantly, I knew I had to share what I learned about myself to help other people. I believe that we sometimes attract people who are similar to us, and in doing so, I attract many people

Chapter 7

Establishing a Baseline for Your Physical and Mental Care

I previously mentioned that once we understand the causes of depression (the why or reasons), we are better able to combat them. The ultimate goal of this book is for you to manage your depression and move on to a healthier, happier lifestyle.

I will admit that within the last fifteen years, I tried at least five different medications without relief of my symptoms of depression. In addition, I believe a few of the medications ended up making me feel worse. One caused an allergic reaction that sent me to the emergency room, another caused me to behave aggressively, and I even experienced a deepened state of depression with one of the medications. I am not speaking against medication, but if they are not for you or you do not want to take them, there are other options, and those options are plentiful.

When dealing with depression, you may need to explore many solutions before finding what works for you. I tend to favor natural practices, such as earthing, sun gazing, sunbathing, natural supplements, and minerals.

The foundation for survival for all humans is food and water. No one can survive long term without consuming food and drinking

27

some type of liquid. The body will lose energy and begin to shut down through starvation and dehydration permanently. I have taken a variety of nutrition classes and will not speak as a nutritionist but will say that a proper diet is probably the number one thing you can do to maintain a healthy body and mind.

There are plenty of studies on the benefits of food consumption. I have chosen to consume a meatless diet for the last four years and believe that this diet is what benefits me the most. On special occasions, I may eat seafood. You have to consume what works for you, and I believe that you can have a healthy diet by consuming things in moderation.

I try to avoid animal products, such as meat, eggs, and dairy at all costs. I consume as many fruits and vegetables as I can. I stay away from white breads, sugars, and rice. I do believe that organic foods are better due to reduced pesticide exposure and support the belief that we should consume six small meals a day versus three large ones.

Diet will always be a subjective topic for people, and this is why I feel that all roads lead back to moderation. Maintaining a healthy diet helps you maintain a healthy mind. I do believe that "you are what you eat," and if your diet is unhealthy, your body and mind will also become unhealthy. Depression can be a side effect of an unhealthy diet, body, and mind.

Make sure that you get enough water every day. Never forget how important it is for you to consume water. Although scientists debate the actual number, our bodies are at least 60% water. If we use water to clean the outside of our bodies, why would we not use it to clean the inside of our bodies? Remaining hydrated is necessary for combating any illness, including depression. Our organs do not function properly when the body is dehydrated. This includes the brain.

are the ones you know you have and the ones you do not know or acknowledge that you have.

There are times when we are aware that we have a problem, but we have too much pride to admit that we are struggling with something like depression. Other times it may be painful to admit. It takes an honest and humble person to admit that they have any problem, and recognizing you are depressed demonstrates that you are honest and humble enough to move forward with healing yourself.

Sometimes you may be afraid of admittance, but I want you to have the courage to complete this step and know that you will be better in the end, regardless of what might be holding you back from admitting and accepting that you are depressed. You must learn to pay attention to yourself as well. We tend to pay attention to everyone around us and never pay attention to ourselves and how we actually feel. Listening to yourself is a form of self-awareness, which we will address in the chapters to come.

We will begin our journey with admittance and acceptance. Admitting you are depressed is something you can do right here, right now. I prefer that you are alone and in a quiet spot; however, it does not matter where you are. Whether you are in a bathroom, your vehicle, or your bed getting ready to go to sleep for the night, allow yourself to feel and understand the words that you are about to speak or write down.

Close your eyes and simply think to yourself, "I admit that I am depressed or that I have suffered from depression." If you feel that thinking to yourself is awkward, you can also write your admission down at the end of this chapter, on a piece of paper, in a journal, or a dated planner. You will then speak aloud, "I admit that I am depressed. I accept that I am depressed, and I want to heal from depression." Again, if speaking these words aloud makes you feel uncomfortable, write them down.

Think about what you verbalized or wrote. For those of you who know how, it is a great idea to implement meditation in this step. If you do not know how to meditate, you can imagine as a substitution. Meditate or think about your admission, your acceptance, and, most importantly, that you want to heal from depression.

Envision how you look and feel in a world with little to no feelings of sadness. Spend five to fifteen minutes imagining, thinking, or meditating on your admission, acceptance, and your future happiness. I want you to have clarity that you are depressed and a sense of calmness that you are going to begin a journey leaving you with a better state of mind than when you began.

There is no reason to do this step more than once. When you have admitted and accepted that you are depressed and acknowledged and envisioned that you want to get better, you can move on to our next step. You may continue to read the next chapter if you would like. When I began this process, I started with the admit/accept/acknowledge step just before I went to bed, and I stopped there.

I found it soothing to fess up to my state of depression and meditate on the idea of getting better. I started the next step the day after, but as I mentioned, it is entirely up to you how fast you get into the additional steps. Either way, I want you to know that you have my support, and I want to see you succeed in this entire process.

Admit, Accept, and Acknowledge Exercise

_____
_____
_____
_____
_____

Were you able to accept, admit, and acknowledge that you are or have been depressed at some point in your life?
_____

What did you imagine life would look like with little to no depression?
_____
_____
_____
_____
_____
_____
_____
_____
_____

Chapter 9

Step 2

Expressing Gratitude and Displaying Acts of Kindness

GRATITUDE

When I was a little girl, my granny always told me to be grateful. She suggested I be grateful to God, grateful for the food I ate, the clothes I wore, and the roof over my head. She would tell me, "Tiffany, be grateful. There is always someone else, worse off than you." She would continue, "Be grateful. Someone else would love to be in your shoes."[9] The words are from a gospel song she loved. I did not understand what she meant as a child, but in my adulthood, those words mean a lot to me.

---

[9] *Hawkins, Walter. "Be Grateful." Lite Records, 1978*

My grandmother was telling me to show gratitude. Gratitude is *the state of being grateful, thankful.*[10] There is a ton of research that confirms that showing gratitude can make you happier in life. A wellness coach by the name of Natalie Ledwell introduced me to the idea of showing gratitude, and I found that expressing gratitude made me feel better. According to *Psychology Today*, "Psychologists found that, over time, feeling grateful boosted happiness and fostered both physical and psychological health, even among those already struggling with mental health problems."[11] Their studies showed that practicing gratitude reduced the use of words expressing negative emotions and shifted inner attention away from negative emotions such as resentment and envy.

"Brain scans of people assigned a task that stimulated expression of gratitude showed lasting changes in the prefrontal cortex that heightens sensitivity to future experiences of gratitude," which supports the idea that gratitude provides us with positive stimulation within the brain and positive emotions.

From experience, I have learned that one of the fastest ways to produce positive emotions within myself is to show gratitude. At the end of this chapter, I want you to pause and take a minute to think of three things you are grateful for. Many of us demonstrate gratitude daily for being alive and healthy, but some of us fall short by thinking of other things we want when we could be grateful for the things we have.

---

[10] *"Giving Thanks Can Make You Happier" Healthbeat. https://www.health.harvard.edu/healthbeat/giving-thanks-can-make-you-happier (accessed February 6, 2020)*
[11] *"Giving Thanks Can Make You Happier" Psychology Today, https://www.health.harvard.edu/healthbeat/giving-thanks-can-make-you-happier (accessed February 8, 2020)*

Depression can often make us feel like there are no reasons to be grateful. The good news is that there are numerous ways to express gratitude and plenty of reasons to be grateful. A few examples include:

- Expressing to a child, spouse, or significant other how much you appreciate them.
- In the workplace, tell your coworkers how grateful you are for their hard work or acknowledge when someone does something to ease your workload.
- If you are a supervisor, give your employees a small bonus or time off. You can do something as small as leaving a post-it note saying thank you.

Each day I want you to find a way to express gratitude. You do not have to come up with over-the-top ways when completing this step. Keep this process as simple as possible. The goal is for you to begin having positive emotions in your life, which will help combat your depression.

Make sure to use your planner, journal, or notebook to write down one thing that you are grateful for each day. You can do this at the beginning or end of the day. Try a few of the examples I explained or come up with some of your own. I want you to do this for at least thirty days, and if you can go on for sixty to ninety days or indefinitely, that is even better.

Remember that we already addressed commitment. To change your state of mind for the better, you must commit to this process. If you practice this step correctly, the changes in your overall mental state will improve, allowing you to manage your depression.

Pay attention to how expressing gratitude makes you feel. Do you feel happier or notice that you feel better when thinking of things you are grateful for? Showing gratitude is one of the steps I have made a habit, and it completely changed my state of mind for the better. It is one of the steps that help me manage my depression.

As I came up with this process, I would show gratitude by writing down the things I was grateful for each day. I committed to this process for at least sixty days, which helped me create a new habit. I no longer write down my feelings of gratitude. For me, this evolved into expressing my gratitude each morning when I wake up. Sometimes I lay in bed and do it; other times, it is a mental drill when I am taking a shower or brushing my teeth. It is a habitual process, and I am used to doing it because it sets the tone for my mind and my day.

I want you to start writing down what you are grateful for each day. After that, you can graduate to accomplishing this as a mental drill. If you are a person who prays daily, you can also use this time to express what you are grateful for.

ACTS OF KINDNESS

Displaying acts of kindness is similar to showing gratitude. You can display acts of kindness with family, friends, and even strangers. One of my favorite examples to use is when I am in my car in line at Starbucks. Sometimes when I pull up to the window, the cashier tells me that the person in the car ahead of me paid for my order. What a win! It has happened to me a few times, and the results are the same. I get a warm, happy feeling inside, and my mood instantly changes.

I am almost ashamed to admit, but the last time this occurred, I was thinking of some rude thoughts about the driver in front of me. I felt like he ordered the entire store. I was in line for a long time, and it seemed like the barista handed him fifty iced coffees and ten bags. I wanted him to get out of the way so that I could make it to work on time.

I pulled up to the window and whipped my debit card out as fast as I could only to hear the words, "The gentleman in the car ahead of you paid for your order." Can you imagine how I felt? I was ashamed of myself. I drove away, and I thought, *Wow, how KIND of that person*. Although I felt like a jerk, his act of kindness completely changed my mood for the better. The gentleman's good deed caused me to feel positive emotions immediately.

I recall another instance when the same scenario occurred. I was not in an impatient mood this time around. I pulled up to pay for my order, and the same feel-good words were spoken, notifying me that the driver in front of me took care of my order. It gave me an instant joyous high, and I decided to pay it forward by paying for the order behind me. The driver of the car behind me chased me down. She rolled her window down and screamed "Thank you" with a huge smile on her face. Her expression of gratitude made me extremely happy.

Simply recalling these two acts of kindness causes feelings of pleasure at this very moment. I am typing with a smile on my face. This is how displaying acts of kindness works. There is some "feel-good" in this ordeal for you as well as the recipient. Acts of kindness are contagious or transferable from one person to the next. I am sure that when someone does something nice for you, it makes you want to "pay it forward," and recalling the memories of the occurrences causes us to feel elation.

It is important to display acts of kindness without having an ulterior motive. This is not where we want to "kill them with kindness." Negativity is not part of this equation. We do not want to give to get or give to receive. Displaying acts of kindness is something we want to do to stimulate positive emotion in others and ourselves because your actions immediately improve the mood of all parties involved.

Offer to hold the door for someone coming in behind you, tell someone how nice he or she looks, or leave a nice note on your receipt when you tip for a meal. You can also display acts of kindness in secret, and your actions can be as small or as grand as you would like.

During the beginning of the pandemic, I bagged food up that I knew we would not use and took it to a homeless community. The food would have eventually spoiled and I would have discarded it into the trash receptacle. Someone needed something I did not want and could use it. It felt good to assist people in need. They were grateful for the food and offered to share it with other families who were homeless.

I am sure there are ideas you can come up with that will leave you and the person you choose to display the actions to with positive emotions.

If displaying acts of kindness is something new for you, I want you to be deliberate with this step for the next thirty days. Remember that you do not have to use a lot of time, energy, and resources when displaying acts of kindness.

Similar to showing gratitude, displaying acts of kindness serves to help improve your mental health. This method will help you combat depression by producing positive emotions.

There is a beautiful quote by Morgan Freeman, which states, "We can change the world by one random act of kindness at a time." I honestly believe this quote and that acts of kindness make life about others versus us, which can be therapeutic. Force yourself out of your comfort zone and do nice things you would normally not do. I guarantee this step will make you feel much better.

Gratitude and Kindness Exercise

List the top three reasons why you are grateful.

_____
_____
_____
_____
_____
_____

When thinking of the reasons you are grateful, does it cause positive feelings and emotions? Explain how those thoughts make you feel.

_____
_____
_____
_____
_____
_____

Will you commit to writing down your feelings and experiences with gratitude and your acts of kindness for at least thirty days? You are welcome to go as long as you would like. The longer the better.

Chapter 10

Step 3

Practice Optimism versus Pessimism

"It's only a bad day, not a bad life."[12] This is the perfect example of having an optimistic outlook on life. I am a Master Resiliency Trainer for the Army, and the term we use when referring to seeing the good even when something is bad, is called "hunting the good stuff." It simply equates to training yourself to think positive thoughts versus negative ones. Look for the good in all things versus looking for the bad.

I understand that it is easier said than done, but practice makes perfect, and forming new habits take time. My overall quality of life and state of mind improved when I chose to view things from an optimistic perspective rather than from a pessimistic one. One of the strangest things I have learned about myself is that I tend to think about things from a negative perspective before seeing any of the positive aspects.

I am still on the journey of learning all about myself, but I believe that I see things from a negative perspective because I was raised around so much negativity. I believe for me; it is a case of nurture

---

[12] *Johnny Depp; unsourced*

versus nature. At some point in life, we learn what things work for us and what things do not. I can tell you that I have not benefitted in any way from being a pessimist.

"Negative Nancy or Nick" thinking will not help you combat your depression in any way.

When I began to force myself into optimism, it was painful and still is. It is difficult to change forty years of pessimistic behavior and thinking. Still, it is possible. You will want to learn how to behave in optimism rather than pessimism because otherwise, you will make yourself vulnerable to falling into depression with negative thinking or the way you react to life's circumstances. My bouts with depression often began with pessimistic thinking.

In this step of the Combating Depression process, I want you to commit to two actions. First, when you catch yourself thinking negative thoughts (stinking thinking), I want you to force yourself to think about something positive. This is redirecting or refocusing your negative thinking. This will be a challenge, but it is very doable if you desire a positive change in your life.

If you are thinking about how terrible your day is going, how much you hate your boss or any other negative thoughts, stop yourself and begin to think about something good that happened, or anything positive. You can implement what you have learned about gratitude as well.

Trust me; there has to be one good thing you can think of and concentrate on. Think how beautiful the weather is, or how refreshing it would be to take a nice long shower after a long day. Please work extra hard to be self-aware so that you can identify your negative thoughts and turn them into positive ones. You must do this habitually for this step to work.

As previously mentioned, showing gratitude, and displaying acts of kindness will help you in this step because they are both optimistic ways of thinking. This is why you need to stick with all of the steps in the Combating Depression process. We make time for the things we find important, and changing your mental thought process is both necessary and important. Change also does not come overnight, nor without repetition.

I do not mean to chastise you, but I do want you to give this step a serious attempt. You can give me any negative example, and I can provide you with an optimist or pessimist way of thinking about that circumstance. For example, "I had a terrible time at work." The optimistic way of thinking about that situation might be, "I had a rough day today, but when I get home, having a nice shower will be so relaxing and refreshing." When implemented correctly, training yourself to recognize the positive versus the negative thoughts in your mind aids you in managing depression.

Recognize that you are in charge of creating a positive state of mind and environment that you desire. Remember that you are also in charge of the negativity you allow in your life, whether it is from internal or external sources. We can indeed make ourselves miserable, and you have to be honest about what you are doing to contribute to your own negative thinking.

This was a frustrating process for me, but I committed to writing down and focusing on my positive thoughts at least once a day. To be honest with you, I got sick of myself, and that is where change began with my negative thinking. I want you to become more aware of your negative thoughts so that you can transform them into positive ones.

Be easy on yourself during this process and realize that you may not be where you want to be mentally as far as thinking positive thoughts, but you will eventually improve. Even if there are small improvements in your positive outlooks and mental state, those thoughts will contribute to helping you avoid depression.

Begin the process of working diligently to improve your shortcomings in being optimistic versus pessimistic. This was one of the toughest steps for me, and it may be the same for you. Pessimism was one of the mental qualities that I disliked the most about myself, and with this step, I found that I learned to pause to redirect my thoughts. The journaling and meditation at least once a day, also helped me train my mind to feel positive thoughts, which I enjoy more than feeling upset, angry, or pessimistic.

Keep at this step until it becomes a habit, and do not get disappointed if it takes you months or even years to improve in this area. The goal in this step is for you to become aware of those pessimistic thoughts, look at things from an optimistic point of view, ponder on the positive thoughts, and naturally combat depression in doing so.

Chapter 11

Step 4

Unpacking Your Emotional Baggage

We have all heard the term "baggage." People sometimes describe their partners as scarred or damaged. This means that their partners suffer from a previous hurt that they may have brought into their relationship. Trust is a big one. In your current or previous relationship, you may have experienced infidelity. If you move on with a new partner, and you do not deal with the previous hurt and pain of infidelity, you may begin to display signs of insecurity, or lack of trust (emotional baggage) with your current partner, eventually leading your relationship into chaos and dysfunction.

The hurt does not always have to stem from infidelity, but this is one of the common causes of emotional baggage. Anything a person does to violate your trust can cause you to carry emotional baggage if you hold on to the hurt. The best way I can describe emotional baggage is as any negative experience that continues to affect how you currently behave.

I believe an incident creates emotional baggage and that it can lead to depression. There is always a cause (physical abuse) and effect (PTSD). Although there are many different types of emotional baggage, I will briefly discuss anger, fear, and guilt to give you a few examples of what they may look like. Keep in mind that what

47

we think we see as emotional baggage could also be a sign of other mental health disorders.

ANGER

We tend to pack our emotional baggage with a lot of anger. It is the negative emotion that I believe we carry around the most. A lot of us are "angry at the world" many times for reasons we do not understand. We lash out, overreacting to our circumstances in anger without a justifiable reason. For some of us, anger is our most prominent emotion. Anger is also a symptom of depression.

Anger can stem from childhood hurts or a variety of different sources. It is a normal emotion for all of us. The continual expression of unwarranted anger is emotional baggage that we must address and resolve when attempting to manage our depression.

FEAR

We all know what fear feels like. Fear is a normal part of life, but if you are afraid because of something you previously experienced, then you may be experiencing a symptom of emotional baggage. Some people will not leave bad relationships due to the fear of being alone or that they will not find another partner.

This type of fear might stem from previous abandonment. The cause is previous abandonment, and the effect is the unwillingness to leave a bad relationship for fear of being alone. This type of fear is unhealthy because one is willing to suffer negative abuse to feel what they see as the comfort of not being alone.

You have heard people say, "I do not deal with Aquarius men or Leo women." If you asked them why they felt this way, and they were willing to give you an honest answer, they would likely talk about someone who hurt them in the past. They are still carrying emotional baggage (hurt, pain, or lack of trust), and they fear being hurt again.

GUILT

Some individuals blame themselves for their failed relationships, living their lives allowing guilt to dictate their unwillingness to move on or into a new relationship. Guilt is a form of self-punishment for past choices that we regret, or feel were mistakes or accidents.

Guilt is emotional baggage that can cause depression and a lot of internal pain, leaving you to live a life where you are not happy with yourself or even with living. Guilt may cause depression. The cause (I cheated on the best woman I ever had). Effect (I do not deserve to have a rewarding relationship because I messed things up with my previous partner).

Any type of baggage will get heavy if carried long enough, and emotional baggage is no exception. The pain of the past still affects us, and many people are unable to start experiencing new, lasting, fulfilling relationships because they are dragging around yesterday's pain, and applying it to today's circumstances.

A new person cannot get into your heart because it remains occupied by someone who is long gone or far removed from your life. You are still living with and carrying around the hurt, which can drive you or keep you in a state of depression.

Although I used relational issues to explain emotional baggage, there are many other examples. You might carry a grudge against a boss who failed to recommend you for a promotion. You might live a life of shame for getting caught cheating in a relationship. You may still harbor anger towards a relative or friend who hurt or betrayed you.

Understand that you do not have to hold on to the emotional baggage caused by these situations. In doing so, you are preventing yourself from moving on in life because of the scar tissue of past relationships or incidents. In many instances, we are still dealing with emotional baggage, and if it involved an individual, they have most likely moved on to their "happily ever after."

You must let go of the emotional baggage to combat or move past the depressive state in your life. You have heard the saying "forgive, but do not forget." Sometimes it is healthier for our state of mind if we both forgive and forget. Let go of the emotional baggage that is causing you regret, shame, pain, guilt, and fear. I understand that this is not easy, but nothing about holding on to something that hurt us or that we lost helps us combat depression.

Here are a few things you can do to unpack your emotional baggage.

FORGIVE YOURSELF

It will not be easy, but like every process that I have mentioned, if you want something, you will go for it, and you will do it. Forgiving yourself is a necessary part of unpacking your emotional baggage. Allow yourself to reflect over your past circumstances and accept that the things that have hurt you, are now in the past and that is where they should remain.

Forgive yourself for any wrongs you have committed against other people. Stop judging yourself and realize that there is nothing you can do about the past. A relative of mine always says that "life is choice-driven." Understand that you may not have made all the best choices in life, but you have made some good ones too.

Do not allow fear to dictate your life. Do not allow anything in life to scare you. Instead, face your fears. Do not fear failure—make attempts. Do not fear people or circumstances—confront them (in a healthy manner).

FORGIVE OTHERS

Stop allowing past relationships to dictate your future behavior. If someone in a past relationship hurt you, whether by abuse, infidelity, or abandonment, attempt to move past that relationship. It does not matter if it is an ex-lover or a family member. You must forgive that person and move on without them.

Release the pain they caused you by sending them an email or text message explaining how you feel, that you forgive them, and you are moving on. You have to really mean this. If you have no contact with the individual or the person is deceased, write a letter to them anyway, forgive them, and move on.

Release any anger that you may harbor toward another person. Let go of the negative memories you keep replaying in your head. Do not continue to carry emotional baggage around in your suitcase. Instead, unpack it because it is preventing your journey of healing. When you feel like you are broken because of the baggage you carry, I want you to remember, "breaks in life are places where the light can shine in," and you can combat your depression by unpacking your emotional baggage.

Emotional Baggage Exercise

What types of emotional baggage do you have that you need to unpack?

_____

_____

_____

_____

_____

Write a brief note to yourself explaining that you accept that your past is not perfect, and that you forgive yourself for anything you may be holding against yourself.

_____

_____

_____

_____

_____

Will you be able to forgive others in the process of unpacking your emotional baggage?

_____

If required. Write a note to the person that you need to forgive as described in this chapter.

Chapter 12

Step 5

Establishing Boundaries

Let me begin with a short story, where I almost let people push me to my breaking point in my life. I am currently a Human Resources officer, and I specialize in providing personnel support to my organization. This type of job is extremely taxing. People come to you when they have issues or need things fixed. There is always an "I need," or "can you." People do not drop by my office just to say hello or see how I am doing. I am in the business of serving customers.

A few years ago, I got myself into big trouble by attempting to help everyone at my job with everything they needed. It did not matter what time they came by my office, or if they sent me a text during my off-hours. I am the type of woman that loves to help anyone I can, and I got used to taking care of the needs of others while neglecting my own.

I will give myself the credit that is due and say that, as far as job performance goes, I knocked it out of the park. However, for my co-workers, this was not enough. No matter how hard I worked to help an organization of nearly 250 people, it was not enough. I was the lead in my office, solely responsible for life insurance updates, drafting and submitting performance evaluations, ensuring financial records were up to date, and assisting with pay issues. This was no easy task for the number of people I was responsible for servicing.

At this job, my assistance was always required. During this time, I had great supervisors who I could rely on to support me with anything I needed. My co-workers, on the other hand, treated me like a mother and, at times, a maid. They always needed something, wanting their "poor planning to become my emergency."

There was a lot of whining and crying when they had pay issues or if they wanted better evaluations than what they had received. Someone always needed something, and it did not matter if I was walking into my office, going to my car to go home, or even at the grocery store shopping with my family. People would stop me to ask about human-resource-related inquiries or submissions they processed in my office.

I had a team of soldiers whom I worked with. Most paperwork would start with them, and my co-workers were not satisfied with that. So, they would come directly to me, and I never turned them away. I always served them with a smile and took care of their needs. I worked long, hectic hours while raising three children as a single parent attempting to keep up with everything it takes to parent children.

Eventually, my co-workers began to send me text messages and call me at home during off-duty hours concerning their work-related issues. Sometimes I would answer, other times not. You had better believe that if I did not answer, they would catch me coming to work when getting out of my car. They would walk me to my office talking about the work-related issues they wanted me to resolve.

All of the stress wore on me. Most days, I could not get into my office, put my things down, and get comfortable. Someone was already in my office asking for help. I could not eat my lunch in peace. I began to close my door during lunch to eat and try to relax and guess what happened. They would knock on the door while I was eating and expected me to help.

This job and my co-workers sent me into a state of depression, but can you guess the reason? It was because I allowed their behavior to have a negative effect on me. I failed to set boundaries for my co-workers, so they ran me over. I began to feel angry and upset with my co-workers and feared I would lash out at some point. I started hating my job and wanted to hide from the people I worked with.

I was so stressed and depressed that I had to seek counseling. I was going insane from my work environment. My counselor helped me understand that I could not please everyone and could not let people disrespect my time or my space. She was the first person to introduce me to boundaries and advised that I establish them immediately. I had to draw a line in the sand, and I did. Most importantly, the boundaries worked and helped ease my state of depression.

I want you to understand that drawing boundaries comes with the territory of being vocal, and this is something I failed at miserably. I had to learn to open my mouth and tell my co-workers that they would have to wait for my team to process their paperwork. They could not meet me at my car and walk me into my office discussing their issues. They could not call or text me after work hours concerning their evaluations—I had a family to take care of.

My counselor explained to me that if employees came to my office during lunch, I did not have to open the door, and even if they said, "I know you are in there"—which they did—I did not have to answer. I realized that I was human, not some servant, and I deserved to take a break and eat in peace, just as they did. You may think that what I am describing is simple and that it is common sense, but it is not.

Boundaries are important. You can apply them to any area in your life. You do not let people misuse, mistreat, or disrespect you, and you must learn to be vocal about it. There are times when you will have to speak up and let people know what you find offensive, that you are establishing a boundary, and you must commit to that boundary for this step to be effective.

When dealing with demanding co-workers, this step can be difficult, but you must always remain professional, courteous, and respectful. Do not stoop to the level of being unkind, childish, or passive-aggressive when establishing boundaries in your life. This step serves to protect you from experiencing the hardship I did, which led me to experience angry, aggressive, and depressing emotions.

You may have to explain your stance to people who violate your boundaries. I often experienced co-workers who would drop by the office for casual conversation. I honestly could not afford to lose time at this job. There were time-sensitive projects that required completion before the end of the day, and the employees who stopped by robbed me of precious time, meaning that I would either have to stay late or come into work earlier. Staying late or coming in early cut into the time I had to go home and cook and get my children ready for the next day, or it cut into the amount of time I had for sleep and my exercise routine the following day.

Simply inform them that you come to work to perform a job. I explained that casual conversations were not possible for me.

People are not entitled to your time. Do not feel guilty for making time for yourself and ensuring you keep your mental health in a good place.

Instilling boundaries does not only apply to your co-workers. You must use this step with relatives, significant others, friends, and strangers. I often see boyfriends and girlfriends calling each other out of their names, or they are disrespectful to one another in some way. If things like this happen to you, you must be vocal enough to tell the disrespectful individual that you do not like what they are doing or how they are talking to you, and you will not tolerate it. If the negative actions do not stop, the next chapter will help.

I will give you another example of a case where I had to use this step. One of my neighbors had no boundaries for her three minor sons. She would let them come outside as early as 7:00 a.m. They would jump on their father's car until its roof caved in, slide down his windshield, take their footballs, and continuously smash them into other neighbors' cars. The three boys began to play directly in front of my home. They would come behind the bushes, walk right up to our bedroom windows, and look inside.

The neighbor obviously did not believe in setting boundaries for her children, so they displayed no boundaries with any of the individuals in my neighborhood. One day, one of the small boys (less than two years old) came on my porch and attempted to climb up on one of our adult-sized bikes. Of course, I went outside and said something to the mother, and yes, she was upset and defensive of her boys. This situation could have played out in a way that would leave me liable and possibly financially responsible if the bike fell on her son.

The boys made so much noise and behaved in such a barbaric manner for about a year before I said anything. There I was, wanting to move out of a home I purchased because of my neighbors when I could have vocalized how I felt a long time ago.

I disliked living next to them so much; I was considering taking a loss to sell my home and move. Her children were causing me frustration, anger, and even anxiety. I also have trouble sleeping and was getting less rest with them already outside during the wee hours of the morning.

Eventually, I got the homeowners' association (HOA) involved, and that was my attempt at establishing boundaries. On another particular day, when her children were disturbing the neighborhood, I went outside to confront her. I made sure that I was cordial but explained to her that I previously contacted the HOA, and they advised me to call the non-emergency number for the police. I informed her that I would hate to get law enforcement involved, but I was at the point of no resolve.

Things improved tremendously, and I attribute it to being vocal and establishing boundaries. I requested she kept her children out of my front yard and off my property for their safety. I drew a line in the sand and let her know that I would not tolerate this disrespectful behavior, and although she told me to "do what I needed to do," it worked.

Remember that "you teach people how to treat you"[13] and to establish boundaries is to protect yourself from the suffering that will cause or increase depression. Our goal is to remove anything from our lives that contributes to additional stressors that may lead to depression. This even includes answering phone calls or social media inboxes. Fully understand that your time belongs to you, and you have the right to share it as you see fit.

---

[13] *Staff, Phil. "Life Law #8: We Teach People How to Treat Us," Dr. Phil, February 6, 2004, https://www.drphil.com/advice/life-law-8-we-teach-people-how-to-treat-us (accessed February 8, 2020).*

Remember to establish a voice for yourself and respectfully inform your family (including children), friends, neighbors, and even strangers when they cross your boundaries. I honestly believe that sometimes people are not aware when they are crossing your boundaries, but often they do know. There will never be a question in their minds if you speak up and let them know, ultimately protecting yourself from unnecessary stressors.

Setting boundaries is one of my favorite and most effective ways to protect myself healthily. It is one of my most preferred methods of combating future depression and should be used whenever necessary.

Establishing Boundaries Exercise

What relationship or roles in your life leave you feeling drained due to a lack of boundaries? Examples might be your job or overextending yourself to others (includes family).

_____

_____

_____

_____

What actions can you take that will help give you peace of mind, protect your time, and provide you with personal space?

_____

_____

_____

_____

Are you committed to the process of establishing boundaries for your wellbeing? If so, what is the first boundary that you are going to implement?

_____

_____

_____

Chapter 13

Step 6

Terminate Toxic Relationships

"Some of the most toxic people in our lives come disguised as family and friends." I cannot find the origin of this quote, but life will teach you how true of a statement this is. Most often, the people who cause the most pain, hurt, and confusion in our lives are the individuals who are/were the closest to us.

During my life, people would do things to hurt me, and I not only forgave them, I frequently made excuses for their poor behavior. I allowed this negative cycle to continue for several reasons, and what this boils down to is: I accepted their behavior. We have all heard that it is the right thing to "turn the other cheek," or extend grace. Many religions teach us to forgive those who mistreat us because they believe that it is what God would do.

I do not want to make this about religion, and I will not tell you how to react to the people in your life who cause you to experience mental anguish. I will tell you what worked for me. I do not believe that anyone should let another individual hold a negative influence in their life, and I do not allow people to subject me to negativity in any capacity.

I did not arrive at this decision overnight, but in hindsight, I look at my decision as a simple one. I do not want anyone in my life that brings ANY darkness into it. I emphasize any because I mean it to the core of my soul. I am overprotective of my energy and myself, and I advise others to do the same because it is working so well for me.

Recently I found out that one of my close relatives was telling other family members that I was saying negative things about them. This relative would come to me and tell me that other relatives were speaking poorly about me. In reality, she was lying to and on all of us. I did not understand why she would do this because we were so close, and I loved her dearly. It is as if she wanted my relatives and me to be at odds with one another.

Numerous incidents similar to this incident had occurred over the years. I felt hurt, betrayed, and angry, but felt there was nothing I could do to stop her negative behavior.

I decided to terminate this relationship and establish boundaries with this individual. I no longer wanted to continue to feel angry concerning the negative circumstances I experienced from our relationship, and I did not want to fight with her because I knew there were slim chances she would admit she was wrong and change her behavior.

For years I was naïve believing this person would return the love that I gave her in the same fashion. I made excuses for her behavior and, at times, was in denial that I was receiving the short end of the stick in the relationship. Although challenging, I had to decide that I did not want to experience this individual's toxicity. I terminated the relationship to protect myself.

Years ago, I recall Maya Angelou speaking on television. She said something that changed my life and the way I dealt with people. Most of you are familiar with her astounding quote, "When someone shows you who they are, believe them the first time."[14] I rehearsed this quote in my mind and promised myself I would live by it.

Do not give any individual another chance to mistreat you. Do not believe that they subjected you to abuse or negativity because they could not help themselves, or they did not mean to. If someone mistreats you, the first time might be an accident, but the second time is intentional. I will not blame you for another person's behavior, but I believe that people will mistreat you if you allow them to, and if you allow them to, it becomes your fault. I learned the hard way that the only person who could stop someone from abusing me was me. I am referring to all types of abuse: nonverbal, verbal, mental, and physical. This is a challenging step, but I believe that you can succeed at it. You must believe in yourself and decide that you will terminate toxic relationships. This is another step I found to be beneficial while dealing with depression.

Terminating toxic relationships means getting rid of your abusive girlfriends, boyfriends, wives, and husbands. And yes, sons, daughters, mothers, fathers, co-workers, and neighbors. Whoever brings intentional abuse or negative energy to you must get out of your life immediately. Please believe me when I tell you that I am not advising you to do things that I do not do in my own life. I have completely implemented this step to protect myself from bad relationships that ended up causing me depression.

This year, I polled a small population of 200 people on Facebook. A shocking 75% (150 people) stated that "relationship issues" were the cause of their depression. I am not a scientist, but there is a strong correlation between toxic relationships and depression.

---

[14] *Maya Angelou Quotes. BrainyQuote.com, BrainyMedia Inc, 2020. https://www.brainyquote.com/quotes/maya_angelou_383371, accessed March 17, 2020.*

Asking you to terminate toxic relationships should be a last-resort solution to help you combat depression. However, many times, this step is a necessity. People should know and understand that if they are abusive, draining, or negative, they do not deserve a place in your life. You can try things, such as counseling, but if a person is showing you that they will not change, and their behavior is damaging to you, why are you still allowing them to cause you harm?

Life is short, with its expectancy at or about seventy-nine years. You do not have time to spend most of it subjecting yourself to abuse from anyone. Protecting your mental health and energy is a necessity when combating depression. You have to admit that there are people who do not deserve to have you in their lives due to the depleted mental state they leave you in after encountering them.

Similar to the previous chapter, "Establishing Boundaries," this step in the Combating Depression process requires that you be vocal. When you have issues with people, you have to make sure that you communicate with them. You cannot resolve the issues you have with individuals if you do not let them know how you feel and what you think. You must explain to friends, family, and your partners what toxic behavior(s) they are subjecting you to, and that if it continues, you are terminating your relationship.

I do understand that there are some of you, who are in abusive relationships, and that explaining this to your partner might put your life at risk. If this is the case, I charge you with finding an effective way to terminate this relationship, not only for your mental wellbeing but also for your personal safety and life. There are many support groups and shelters available for you to receive help and have a safe place to sleep.

No matter how many times your partner professes that they will change, please do not believe them. If they have not changed and continuously subject you to abuse, what makes you think they will change now or in the future? Unless serious intervention takes place, the abuse will continue, and you will remain in a mental state where you are unable to prevent, manage, or overcome depression. I am writing from experience.

Of course, there are many different scenarios regarding the toxic relationships you may experience. You may struggle significantly with family members. I use many examples, hoping that you will relate to my experiences and (as I did) reach solutions in your life. You are ultimately the individual who has to decide to terminate unhealthy relationships.

I have family members who brought nothing but disorder, chaos, and destruction to my life. I love those family members, but I do not benefit from having a relationship with them. I experience hurt every time I deal with them, and I have always expected that "this time it will be different." It took me 35 years to understand that they will never change, and with this understanding, I terminated those relationships.

Other family members talk to me about the individuals, and absolutely nothing has changed. I love them from a distance and wholeheartedly believe that "blood does not make you family; the relationship does," and if you do not treat me with respect and dignity, I cannot associate with you.

My quality of life tremendously improved when I decided to rid my life of toxic individuals and relationships. Sometimes it hurts, but the result (after you get over the pain) is the ability for you to move on in life without the abuse the individual(s) subjected you to. There is no doubt that these situations actually made me a stronger woman. A person is either bringing goodness into your life or the opposite.

When you get used to separating who belongs and who doesn't in your life, it becomes effortless and you see the negativity float out of your life or minimized, which protects you from entering a depressed state. Life is hard enough—you do not need anyone else bringing additional problems and negativity into it.

In this step, I have included both family and friends, and I want you to understand that you do not have to rid people forever. Sometimes people do change—and accepting them back into your life will be up to you—but if they are bringing toxicity into your life, they do not deserve to be part of it, and you should remove them immediately.

When implemented correctly, this step alone solved more than half of the problems that caused my depression, which stemmed from toxic interactions with people. Combating depression requires you to protect your state of mind by surrounding yourself with people who love and are there for you instead of people who want to cross the line and disrespect you. If people are not for you, they are against you. If there are people who claim that they are neutral, those individuals are also against you.

Remember that you are the individual that must put a stop to the toxicity of these relationships. "Never get mad at someone for being who they have always been. Be upset with yourself for not coming to terms with it sooner."[15] Start the process of terminating toxic relationships today. You deserve to live a life of pleasure and positivity, and you cannot do that with toxicity and negativity in your life.

---

[15] *Author unknown*

Terminate Toxic Relationships Exercise

Relationship Evaluation

How does interacting with this person make you feel? Do you have positive interactions with this individual, or are you usually left feeling drained?

_____

_____

_____

_____

Does this individual respect you?

_____

Have you addressed your issues with this individual? Do they want to work with you to improve your relationship?

_____

_____

Would your quality of life improve if you terminated this relationship?

_____

Based on your responses in this exercise, is this a relationship that you should end?

_____

Chapter 14

Step 7

Know Thyself

"Know thyself, for once we know ourselves, we may learn how to care for ourselves."[16] That quote is powerful and enough to begin and end a chapter in one line.

My favorite step and chapter in the Combating Depression process is all about knowing yourself! I hope this step becomes a lifelong process for you. Getting to know and understand myself is the most fulfilling thing I have ever worked at. Though painful at times, this is one of the most beneficial and interesting processes that I have implemented into my life for the long haul. It is one that never ends. My suggestion is that you do the same.

Getting to know yourself is really about self-awareness (the knowledge of self), and this practice might sound strange, but most of us know other people better than we know ourselves, and this is a problem. You have spent all these years with yourself, and you

---

[16] *Socrates; source unknown*

do not intimately know who you are, what you like, where you are headed in life, nor how you will get there. Am I correct?

This process begins with your introduction to you. Many of you will need privacy, and you may want to give your family and friends a small disclaimer that if they hear you speaking to yourself, they should neither be alarmed nor have you committed to the nearest psychiatric ward. Explain to them what you are doing if it makes you more comfortable.

You can begin this step today, but remember that this is a long-term process that will pay enormous dividends for you in the future. The goal in this process is to habitually practice self-awareness and establish mindfulness, which is your thoughts and the observation of the environment that you are in.

I want you to learn as much about you as possible, with the end goal of making yourself a whole person. If you are single, this is the perfect time to begin this process. If you are in a relationship, this is still a beneficial practice that will improve your life and help you combat depression.

You will begin this process by looking at yourself in the mirror at least once a day. You do not have to look at yourself and say something like, "Hello, my name is Irene," but you can if you would like. I want you to look into your own eyes and practice what I refer to as "concentrated self-awareness."

You can have a dialog aloud or mentally by asking yourself things such as:

> "How are you feeling today?"
> "What are you happy about?"
> "What are you upset about?"
> "What are some things you can put in place to make life easier, better, more fulfilling?"

69

- ➢ "What is stopping you from being as happy as you would like to be?"
- ➢ "How does your environment feel, and if it is not comfortable, what can you do to improve it?"

Lastly, and if it is the only thing that you can say, always tell yourself, "I love you."

As I mentioned, if you feel comfortable formulating the questions out loud, you may do so, or you can ask them silently in your mind. I want you to answer your own questions. Your answers will surprise you. When you implement this process correctly, you will learn things about yourself that you did not know as this step allows you to get completely in touch with yourself and what you are feeling.

You do not have to use the mirror each time, but the purpose of this step is to get to know as much about you as you can. Sometimes I use a journal during this step. For example, if I look at myself in the mirror and ask a question, and I get one of the answers I am surprised about, I will write the question and response down. I might ask myself, "What are you upset about?" I then begin to write down why I am upset. You can write long, drawn-out explanations, or simply jot down phrases or words.

Writing your negative feelings down often assists you in sorting through your emotions. It is also a healthy way to prevent lashing out in anger. Journaling has a calming effect that is more beneficial than you remaining upset. If your feelings are negative, use your journal in an attempt to get to the root cause of why you are upset. Allow yourself to acknowledge why you are upset and what you can do in that particular moment to calm yourself.

My therapist often tells me that anger is a projection of fear. In my moments of anger, I have asked myself what I was fearful of. Some of my answers shocked me. Sometimes I was afraid of failing; other times, I was afraid of losing someone, being alone, or not being in control. Understanding your feelings and emotions and why you are feeling such things will assist you in self-mastery. If you know and understand what you feel and why you are feeling a certain way, you can change the negative emotion to a positive one.

Positive self-talk works similarly. Once you realize what you are upset about, you can change the course of your emotions by asking yourself what there is to be happy or appreciative in life for. Begin to journal about your positive experiences, and they should produce positive emotions, which is a win in combating depression—the positive self-talk ties directly with having that optimistic outlook that I described in Chapter 10.

I do realize that life is hectic, and things do not always move at a speed where one can always practice self-talk but, I created the habit of self-talk in my own life and believe it is incredibly healthy. I practiced it so much that it became a habit. I now practice self-talk and mindfulness quietly and almost involuntarily. Many of you may think this is nuts, or others will think I am a quack; however, I honestly believe that this process works if you invest in practicing it.

Learn to be with and understand yourself. You should know you better than anyone else does. You know the person you are around others and the person you are in private. These are usually two different people. We want to make these two people the same. Learn to talk to yourself, regulate, teach, and understand you.

At some point, you have to learn that you must take care of yourself first. When onboard an airplane, what do flight attendants tell you to do when they mention a lack of cabin pressure and oxygen? They tell you to assist yourself first by "securing your mask before assisting others."

The importance of knowing yourself works the same way. How can you give yourself the best in life if you do not intimately know yourself? Look at what occurred during the COVID-19 pandemic. Due to the isolation and quarantine mandates, it is the perfect time to get to know yourself. Many of us were alone, isolated, and socially distanced, and the phase of sheltering in place or isolating ourselves does not seem that it will pass anytime in the near future.

You get to know yourself by doing the things you would normally do with others alone. This means you can take yourself on dates by learning how to go out to dinner and even travel independently. Get comfortable with being you and learning your likes and dislikes. Find those things you love and be simplistic about it. You may discover that you enjoy being in your own company.

Years ago, I was an individual who feared being alone. Going in public to dine alone was out of the question. I worried about what people would think about me. It is sad yet true. I discovered peace, stillness, and tranquility by spending time alone and enjoying the things that I love in my own company.

Take walks, go fishing or sightseeing. Figure out what things you like the most and make them a part of your life's routines. Hike trails, read a book, meditate, use essential oils, get a massage, or cook your favorite meal alone. When you ask yourself what you like, make a list of things, start to do them, and check them off your list.

When I began the step in this process, I learned to block time off just for me by scheduling something once a week at a minimum. Make sure other people know (for example) that on a Friday night, you will schedule your bath or relax time. You can do it every night if you would like. Just remember to make time for you to enjoy your own company.

I would advise against getting into relationships just because you are lonely or for the sake of having someone. Make yourself happy by dating yourself first. It is a more painless process to get to know yourself if you do not have someone around as a distraction.

The process of understanding and learning about myself created success in my combating depression. You can use self-talk to self-regulate panic attacks, bring order to your negative feelings, or simply put yourself in a relaxing state before meditation or bed.

We begin to fulfill ourselves when we know ourselves. Another person should not know you more than you do yourself. There is no other woman I would rather be, and it is because I introduced myself to me and began to know and understand me. It is a beautiful process that I am still working through, and it has enhanced my relationship with others around me.

What are you feeling? Listen to your emotions and feelings and respect them. In other words, allow yourself to feel. Express your feelings in a peaceful, respectful, and healthy manner to release those negative emotions. I have experienced encounters where people have told me that being emotional makes me weak, or that expressing emotions is not healthy for my overall wellbeing. I have witnessed parents say to their children that it is not okay for them to be angry, sad, or upset. We hear parents tell their children, "Hush all of your crying," or "stop being a big baby."

I disagree with these views and believe that not expressing yourself causes emotional and mental damage. If you are not expressing your emotions (in a healthy way), then you are suppressing them. You are stuffing your feelings down; eventually, you might explode with anger.

Practice self-talk, even if it is internal talk. Learn to consistently place yourself in a state of self-awareness by analyzing your thoughts, feelings, attractions, fears, and what you can do to make an overall improvement in your wellbeing. When you understand what causes your mind to experience elation safely, it can become a healthy addiction. You will continuously chase those things that you love and make you feel good.

During the phase of getting to know me, I began to listen to and enjoy new genres of music, and I set new goals concerning new things I wanted to try and experience. I gained an appreciation for nature and found that I have a true appreciation for travel. I learned that I enjoyed being outside, observing the world in the stillness of my own company, and I also began to observe my moods. I control my exposure to things that cause me negative emotions, and I seek to make as many self-improvements in my being as I can.

I want you to do the same. Figure out how to care for yourself better than anyone else. Learn and understand what it takes to master your negative emotions and thinking. Figure out who you are when you are not around others. What are your joys in life? What things do you appreciate the most in life? What new things do you want to learn, and how can you build yourself up, making yourself a stronger individual who loves what they see when they look in the mirror?

The goal in this step is to learn as much as possible about yourself to make yourself as fulfilled in life as possible. Your likes, dislikes, what makes you happy or unhappy, is vital for you to understand because the most important and fulfilling relationship you can ever have is with yourself. You will never be happy with anyone or anything until you are happy with you. I believe the answers to combating depression start with looking within and "knowing thyself."

Chapter 15

Step 8

Be Authentic

It is important to be yourself. Be authentic to yourself and others around you. Be you and never hide who you are or pretend to be someone you are not. I believe that the core of authenticity is self-love and the ability to present the true you to the world.

Most of us can recall being teased as children because of our differences. I was a child with large teeth, and I hated them, suffering from low self-esteem because my classmates called me Bucky Beaver. When I became an adult, I went to the dentist and told him I wanted veneers. He showed me a mirror and told me how beautiful my teeth were. I had the money to make my teeth look how I believed everyone else's teeth looked, and this dentist refused to do it.

I remember crying in his office. He told me I had some of the most beautiful teeth he had ever seen and that people paid to have their teeth look like mine. From that day, I learned to love my teeth and myself more. I really took a hard look at my teeth and saw that yes, they were beautiful, and I would not be acting as my authentic self if I changed my teeth to look like a celebrity's teeth. I was trying to look like a celebrity instead of myself.

I look back and want to hug the old me because I did not realize how great it would be to want to be in my own skin. I no longer use the word celebrity. They are no different from you and me, and we all have something special about us. Today I find value in loving myself just the way I am. Accepting who I am and presenting my true self to others.

Being different is what makes each of us unique and if you love and accept yourself as you are, then it should not matter what anyone thinks of you. Realize that you are beautiful and perfect just the way you are and do not allow anyone to tell you differently. You are beautiful on the inside and out. Recognize your true beauty and love yourself for it.

We are our toughest critics and often live our lives comparing ourselves and listening to others, never realizing that we are good enough. We search for love, affection, attention, and validation in everyone other than ourselves, failing to realize we are the ones that must provide this to ourselves. It is of the utmost importance that we learn to look within before looking to others.

After you get to know yourself and what you love, you must present that person to the world. Being authentic is essentially being yourself. If you spend your life trying to be someone else, you will never be happy because it is not an attainable goal. It amazes me to know that we are so special and intricately created that no person who has ever lived or is living has the same fingerprints. We are all created equal but different, and that is what makes us unique.

We can use one of the current events the world is experiencing today -- 450 years of racism and differences are tearing at the very fibers of a nation. Minorities are treated differently because of the color of their skin. I do not want to make this chapter about racism, but if we look at the topic on a macroscopic level, people treat others poorly because there is insecurity within them. Would you agree?

For you to hurt another individual based on their differences, you would have to be insecure in your own being. For you to maliciously hurt anyone based on prejudice, you would need to have a dislike for yourself. You could not possibly be an authentic person. Lack of authenticity is damaging to us as individuals and the people we come in contact with. You are not aware of your true self, and others are not aware of who you really are.

Most people want others to like them, and they are willing to sacrifice their authenticity to be liked, loved, appreciated, accepted, and even promoted within a job. Being an inauthentic person causes a great deal of internal conflict—or at least it does for me, and this is something I struggled with all of my life.

Most people would describe me as having a serious personality, but once I get to know people, they discover that I am a nice person. I would describe myself as one with a tough exterior or disposition, with a tender and sweet interior or personality. Throughout my life, I would say that I have been one of those women that others do not like initially. I have not figured this out yet, and I must say it feels liberating to say I do not care finally.

I spent the first thirty years of my life, begging, pleading, and asking people to love me. *Please like me. Please come hang out with me. Please talk to me.* There was one reason why the connections between myself and others never flourished, and that was because they wanted me to be somebody I was not. People would say, "Oh you look so mean, you should smile more, you do not look approachable, you are so quiet, you seem stuck on yourself, you do not socialize enough, you think you are too good for us," and the list of negativity runs on.

I have always had the same personality—even as a little girl—and people always saw something wrong with me. There were times when I tried to figure out what was wrong with me. *Why am I the way that I am; why am I different?* I thought that maybe I should be like others, be nicer, smile more, laugh a little. In other words, be fake—be inauthentic. I have never been able to accomplish this. Today I am pleased with myself. Take me as I am or move out of my personal space.

I remember going to work and feeling like once I left the house, I was putting on a mask -- my mask of inauthenticity. It felt terrible by the time I got off work, and before I got home, I had to take my mask off and get out of character. Of course, this contributed to depression. Not being yourself is mentally draining, taxing, and depressing.

This step is more of a plea to ask you to be yourself. I am asking you to do this for your own benefit. Have you heard the saying, "Go along to get along?" You can think of it as peer or social pressure. It is common for children and teens to behave in this manner, but adults do it as well. We do not express our true opinions, thoughts, feelings, or emotions because we want acceptance from others. We suppress who we are and pretend to be something we are not.

Have you ever lied to impress a co-worker, date, mate, friends, or family? Of course, you have. No matter how big or small, we have all portrayed ourselves in ways that were not truthful. We pretend to be what we believe society wants to see, versus being ourselves. In doing so, we suppress who we really are and often lose ourselves through our lack of authenticity.

Suppressing who you are generates negative feelings and emotions and that is unhealthy. The desire to be or act like someone else is a sign that you are unhappy with who you are, and it is unhealthy to live in a world of "monkey see, monkey do." You know of someone who purchased a new home, so you go and buy one. You see someone buy a new car, so you go purchase one. Everyone gets a tongue piercing, and now you have one too. Fads happen, and this is okay. However, it is not okay to never have the ability to make decisions for yourself because you are busy trying to emulate someone else.

I want to use the real-life story of someone I knew who owned a hair salon for nearly ten years. She had a best friend who was envious of her, and instead of being supportive of her salon and proud of her success, she began to tell everyone that she could do the same thing, be successful, and thrive.

Her friend opened her own hair salon and failed in less than six months. I believe this occurred because she was not a student of herself. She did not know or understand herself, and she was not her authentic self. She wanted to be like her best friend instead of using her gifts and talents to succeed in life. She has since admitted that she wanted the success of her friend, but she did not have the same true talent, nor was she willing to put in all the hard work.

It is dangerous to see the world through someone else's eyes rather than your own. We all have our own gifts, talents, and purpose in life. You have to do the hard work of learning about yourself and being yourself so that your vision is always your own and not someone else's. Things are clear when we genuinely manifest from ourselves versus trying to accomplish things because she or he did this or that. No one on this earth has ever succeeded at being someone else.

I know a married pastor who is dating another woman. He is holding online services preaching to his congregation about being authentic, true to themselves, and how he has always been a model husband and father. This individual also performs marriage counseling.

I am not judging him by any means, but he is in no position to instruct people on marriage or morals when he is not living it himself. Most importantly, he is an example of someone who is living a lie. He is not living a life of authenticity.

To be inauthentic is to lie to yourself. To be inauthentic is to fail in life, and I can handle failing at anything other than failing at being me. Being authentic is related to the previous chapter of knowing yourself. Being inauthentic can cause self-hate, and that works directly against our efforts in combating depression. To be an authentic individual is to love yourself for who you truly are. To be authentic is to be courageous. Practicing authenticity is not easy, especially when people do not like who they really are, and they wish they could live as other people.

Being authentic will empower you. Knowing yourself, loving yourself, and being who you truly are generates pride, joy, and self-appreciation. It works against depression. There are no pressures or standards of being someone else because you know and love who you are. You cannot expect to progress in your own life by behaving like someone else, or by acting as if you are someone you are not.

There is a ton of fulfillment in life when you establish your own identity, plans, and visions. This is not to say that others cannot inspire you to act; however, you must make sure your motives are sincerely yours. You do not have to follow the crowd; you do not have to drive a particular car because your neighbor has one or dress a certain way because it is the way so-called celebrities dress.

If you are missing the mark in being your true self, I believe there are a few ways that you can cultivate your authenticity.

- Learn to practice self-love. Begin to love yourself for who you are. Be sure to tell yourself, "I love you" very often.
- Always tell the truth and make truth-telling a healthy habit

no matter what anyone else thinks.
- Make sure that your belief systems and values are yours and not someone else's.

The majority of us can comprehend if we are our authentic selves. We know when we are behaving a certain way because of what our family, friends, or co-workers think, and if we are inauthentic, then we realize we are not happy. I believe that the desire to be and display our true selves is closely related to our happiness, and the happier we are, the more we combat depression.

Being authentic is liberating. No one can take away your authenticity or gift. It is special to know and understand that just like there is no way for you to be another individual, there is no way for any other person to **Be You**. You were not created to be someone else, and I honestly believe your ultimate successes will come from being authentic.

Chapter 16

Step 9

Understanding Your Purpose

I briefly talked about my purpose in Chapter 2. One of the reasons I believe people suffer from depression is because they do not understand their purpose in life. I believe that all of us are born with our own purpose. Before I figured out what one of my purposes in life was, I felt I had little to live for.

Without understanding your purpose or mission in life, it is difficult to have a reason that motivates you to get out of bed in the morning and keep going when you hit those walls in life. Many people who do not understand their purpose have no drive, do not understand their likes, what makes them special, or what their gifts are.

Purpose often provides us with a direction in life and typically gives us a journey to embark on. I naturally get a high from chasing my goals and dreams associated with what I believe my purpose to be, but I recall asking myself for about a year straight. "What is my purpose?" "Why am I alive?" "What am I here for?" These are all depressing questions when you do not have the answers. I began to read books and articles on purpose. What I discovered was that my purpose was related to the loves, joys, and passions in my life, and I believe your passions are related to your purpose.

One of my greatest loves is to help individuals know, understand, and love themselves. I also have a passion for all facets of real estate, which I intend to use as a tool to help people in the near future. I have a strong passion for travel, and I can tell you that each of my passions in life directly connects with my purpose.

If you are not sure what your purpose in life is, I want you to use this step to attempt to identify or gain a better understanding of what your purpose might be. In my experience, I longed to understand why the universe woke me up every day, and most of us experience this feeling. I believe that not knowing your purpose in life can cause you frustration and depression over time.

Think about what your gifts are. Our gifts are our capabilities and talents that come naturally for us. We have all heard of innate talent. Some individuals are born naturally smart, athletic, or possess unparalleled leadership capabilities. There are naturally talented singers, artists, and actors, and then there are individuals who have to put in the hard work of study or practice to become great in certain areas.

I believe that if you are gifted in a certain area, it is closely related to your purpose. We are all gifted in one way or another. Think of children who are obsessed with playing with airplanes from a young age. Many times, these children become pilots. I knew a child who would take apart and put back together anything he could get his hands on. This child knows he wants to be an engineer.

I do not want you to simply think in terms of gifts and talent as in the context of a job or career. However, I do believe you should use your gifts for monetary gain. Our gifts are also for us to give away, which helps us operate within our purpose. There is a healthy balance in how we use our gifts. Attempt to focus on what your gifts are, and I honestly believe they will lead you to your passion and purpose.

Besides a relationship, I want you to also think about what you love and want the most, but fear going after in your life. I believe this is also an indication of your purpose. Fear stops many of us from achieving the very things we dream of.

Operating in understanding our purpose makes for a rewarding life. There is no better feeling in the world than to understand what your purpose is and know that you are on a journey toward fulfilling it. One might ask, how can I use my purpose to combat depression? It is simple. Finding your purpose and following it creates happiness. Happiness combats depression.

Understanding Your Purpose Exercise

What are your greatest talents or gifts?

_____

_____

_____

_____

_____

How can you use your talents or gifts to help others?

_____

_____

_____

_____

_____

What do you love the most in life, but fear acting on?

_____

_____

_____

_____

_____

In answering the questions, are there any actions you can take that will help you use your gifts to help others, start a business, go after something you feared trying, or beginning?

_____

_____

_____

_____

I do not believe that anyone has all the answers when it comes to fulfilling your purpose, but I do believe that once we get an indication of what it might be, we can then begin the journey of having a purpose in our lives and fulfilling that purpose.

Chapter 17

Step 10

Combating Worry

One of the biggest challenges you might run into when combating depression is overcoming worry. Worry is defined as "a state of anxiety and uncertainty over actual or potential problems."[17] *Merriam-Webster* defines worry as "mental distress or agitation resulting from concern usually for something impending or anticipated."

Both definitions describe worry as a response to things that have not occurred. Worry can cause us to feel panicked and anxious. Bouts with worry can lead to anxiety and depression. To combat depression, worrying must be addressed.

Worrying about a relative in the hospital, how you will perform on a test, or how you will make ends meet is normal. Excessive worry is a problem often referred to as anxiety. When your worry becomes excessive, prevents you from getting normal amounts of rest, and interferes with your normal daily routines, you may have a serious problem that requires medical attention. In combating

---

[17] *Lexico US Dictionary," http://lexico.com (accessed March 26, 2020)*

depression, prevention is the key to helping us with our struggles that lead to our unhappiness. Worry is no different.

To some degree, we are all worried about the COVID-19 pandemic. Some of you are unemployed and do not know how you will make ends meet. We are worried what school will look like for our children and how we will keep them safe. Some of us are worried about how this pandemic will affect the housing market. We are worried about the introduction of a vaccine and the requirements of having to take it.

Many of us have family and friends who have had the virus. Some of the people we know required hospitalization; others did not. Some of us lost people that we know and loved to the virus.

Many people are becoming depressed with the lack of freedom to socialize like we used to. You may feel that your rights are being stripped away. We cannot travel for business or vacation as we used to. In Hawaii, we cannot enter stores without a mask. If our relatives are hospitalized, we often cannot see them, and if we are exposed to those who have COVID-19, we must quarantine for up to fourteen days.

All of these ordeals are causing us a massive amount of stress and worry. Many of us are suffering from depression. Like the majority of this book, I am speaking from experience in hopes that my struggles will help you.

I mentioned a few times that I was diagnosed with COVID-19 during what I felt like was the worst time in my life. After experiencing all the worries and anxieties that we are all living through, my worst nightmare became a reality. After over-sanitizing and faithfully wearing my mask, using hand sanitizer, and washing my hands twenty times a day, COVID-19 decided to pay me a visit.

Worry did not subside but became my reality. When I was diagnosed with COVID-19, no amount of worry could save me, and there was no amount of panic that could help me. My doctor told me not to worry because it would cause me additional stress and that I needed my energy to battle my illness. It was at this point that I realized all the things everyone else had always told me.

Worry does not help anything. Worry is natural, but it will not help us and is harmful to our mental health. Worry is not reality. Worry can lead to depression.

Understand your habits of worry so that you can manage them. Realize certain things may be out of your control and that there may be nothing you can do to change what you are worrying about. Find peace in knowing that life will play out how it is supposed to, and you can react to circumstances as they play out. Understand that worry is not a preventative measure.

We are all going through and experiencing the pandemic and societal change throughout the world and we will all get through it together. You can prepare for certain things, but nothing could have prepared the world for what we are experiencing. If you are living in fear of contracting COVID-19, the best thing I can encourage you to do is to fear nothing.

Sometimes fear is healthy, but like worry, it will not help you prepare for or fight the virus. I am not knocking any of the advised preventative measures established for the virus, but I feel the best thing you can do is prepare yourself by maintaining a healthy diet and exercise. This is not only for COVID-19, but life in general.

Limit your worry, anxiety, and depression to keep your mind healthy. Make sure that you get enough rest and sleep. Address and attempt to improve any pre-existing mental or physical health conditions you may have. Exercise, meditate or practice yoga.

Combating depression requires that we learn healthy tools to combat worry.

We have all been through an abundance of issues and problems that we have worried about. Just as we have succeeded with our past issues, we will succeed through the COVID-19 pandemic and any other ordeals we may face, but without worry. Worry does not solve any problems; we often worry about things we cannot solve and sometimes about things that never happen. When worried, keep in the back of your mind that everything will be okay.

Combating Worry Exercise

There are a few questions you can ask yourself when feeling worried. The answers to these questions may help calm you.

Are you safe from hurt, harm, or danger?

_____

Is there anything you can do right now that will affect the outcome of what you are worried about?

_____

What is the best- and worst-case scenario for your situation?

_____
_____
_____
_____
_____

What can you do right now to relax?

_____
_____

Chapter 18

Beginning a New Journey

Although we are at the end of the book, this is the beginning of your journey. Depression defeated me for a long time, while I would lie in bed, not wanting to face life. It took me a long time to fight back. I expected my issues to just go away. I chose to live in deep pain, denial, and acceptance day after day. "Doing things, the same way, and expecting things to change is the definition of insanity."[18]

I suffered in silence and was ashamed and embarrassed to admit I was drowning in sorrow. I was having panic attacks alone and jumping from prescription to prescription and was not getting any results.

I decided I needed to be accountable to myself. I was accountable to my husband, children, friends, relatives, but I was not accountable to myself. Lying in bed feeling defeated and sorry for myself was not the solution.

---

[18] *Albert Einstein; source unknown*

I needed to act and take the steps so I could improve my life. That is when I decided to write down the things I thought might help me get better results in the areas I could be responsible for concerning my depression. I made a commitment to myself and made things right with myself.

This is what I know to be true. It is the people who take action who win in life. It is the people who decide they want new tools and want to form new habits in life that come out on top and who will go on to manage and prevent depression effectively.

One day I tried something new, and it helped. Things look different to me today because I decided to fight for my happiness. Sometimes it takes a coach or a mentor to get to the next level. Sometimes we get stuck, and we need help, a small push forward, or a piece of motivation and encouragement.

Remember that change is a process that does not happen overnight. This journey will take time, commitment, and hard work. You must want to be successful at managing your depression. Know that if I made so many improvements in my life, you can as well.

I hope this book helps you by providing you with tools that make life easier for you to combat depression. Commit to the steps in the Combating Depression process and learn how to be at peace with your past, in love with the present, and excited about your future.

Best wishes to you, and your journey.

COMBATING DEPRESSION

Made in the USA
Las Vegas, NV
11 March 2024

87034603R00059